GUINNESS
RECORD KEEPER

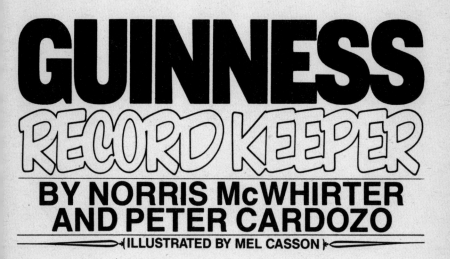

GUINNESS
RECORD KEEPER

BY NORRIS McWHIRTER
AND PETER CARDOZO

ILLUSTRATED BY MEL CASSON

BANTAM BOOKS
TORONTO · NEW YORK · LONDON

GUINNESS RECORD KEEPER
A Bantam Book / published by arrangement with
Sterling Publishing Co. Inc.
All rights reserved.
Copyright © 1979 by Sterling Publishing Co., Inc.
Based on the Guinness Book of World Records
This book may not be reproduced in whole or in part, by
mimeograph or any other means, without permission.
For information address: Sterling Publishing Co., Inc.
2 Park Avenue, New York, N.Y. 10016
ISBN 0-553-M 01204-5

PRINTED IN THE UNITED STATES OF AMERICA

0 9 8 7 6 5 4 3 2 1

PUT YOUR RECORD IN THE GUINNESS RECORD KEEPER

Here's a new kind of fun! Now you can try the things that people do to get into the **Guinness Book of World Records**...and keep a record of how well you do.

How far can you throw a baseball? How high can you build a house of cards? How long can you and your friend play leap frog?

The **Guinness Record Keeper** presents you with 45 different challenges...and the actual **Guinness** record. Try them! Fill in your score and write down the date. There are plenty of spaces for your records so you can try again and again, and better your own score. There's a section for your friends' records, too.

Just remember...you're not supposed to match or even come close to the **Guinness** records, because most of them were set by people who are older, bigger, stronger and have been practising for many years.

But you can have a great time trying to beat your own record or competing against the boy or girl who lives next door or maybe down the block. The important idea is to have fun. Do the best you can...and put **your** record in the **Guinness Record Keeper.**

HOW FAR CAN YOU **THROW A BASEBALL?**

THE GUINNESS RECORD:

Longest Throw. The record for throwing a standard size baseball is 445 feet 10 inches by Glen Gorbaus on August 1, 1957. Babe Didrikson holds the women's record for throwing a ball 296 feet at Jersey City, New Jersey, on July 25, 1931.

MY RECORDS:

_____ FEET _____ INCHES _____ DATE

_____ FEET _____ INCHES _____ DATE

_____ FEET _____ INCHES _____ DATE

_____ FEET _____ INCHES _____ DATE

_____ FEET _____ INCHES _____ DATE

MY FRIEND'S RECORDS:

_____ FEET _____ INCHES _____ DATE

_____ FEET _____ INCHES _____ DATE

THE GUINNESS RECORD:

Swinging. 182 hours (or almost 8 days) is the longest time recorded for swinging without stopping except for rest breaks of 5 minutes after every hour. This record was set by Pia Andersson and Matt Gonzalez of Torrance, California, December 16 to 24, 1977.

MY RECORDS

HOURS	MINUTES	DATE
HOURS	MINUTES	DATE
HOURS	MINUTES	DATE
HOURS	MINUTES	DATE
HOURS	MINUTES	DATE

MY FRIEND'S RECORDS

HOURS	MINUTES	DATE
HOURS	MINUTES	DATE

HOW **LONG** CAN YOU AND YOUR FRIEND PLAY **HOPSCOTCH**?

THE GUINNESS RECORD:

Hopscotch. The record for hopscotch jumping is exactly 48 hours. It was set by two pairs, Robert Calzolari and Mark Pearson, and Bruce Borup and David Black, all of Chelmsford, England, April 28 to 30, 1978.

OUR RECORDS:

_____ HOURS _____ MINUTES ___ DATE

_____ HOURS _____ MINUTES ___ DATE

_____ HOURS _____ MINUTES ___ DATE

_____ HOURS _____ MINUTES ___ DATE

_____ HOURS _____ MINUTES ___ DATE

_____ HOURS _____ MINUTES ___ DATE

THE GUINNESS RECORD:

Spitting. The record for spitting a melon seed is 59 feet 1½ inches and was set in Queensland, Australia, by Brian Dunne on December 11, 1976.

MY RECORDS:

_____FEET _____INCHES _____DATE

_____FEET_____INCHES _____DATE

_____FEET_____INCHES _____DATE

_____FEET_____INCHES _____DATE

_____FEET_____INCHES_____DATE

MY FRIEND'S RECORDS:

_____FEET_____ INCHES_____DATE

_____FEET_____INCHES _____DATE

_____FEET_____INCHES_____DATE

HOW **LONG** CAN YOU **JUMP ROPE** **WITHOUT** STOPPING?

THE GUINNESS RECORD:

Rope Jumping. In Milwaukee, Wisconsin, Rabbi Barry Silberg jumped 50,180 times without stopping for 6 hours.

MY RECORD:
_____HOURS _____MINUTES_____DATE

_____HOURS _____MINUTES_____DATE

_____HOURS_____MINUTES_____DATE

_____HOURS_____MINUTES_____DATE

_____HOURS_____MINUTES_____DATE

MY FRIEND'S RECORD:
_____HOURS_____MINUTES_____DATE

_____HOURS _____MINUTES_____DATE

_____HOURS_____MINUTES_____DATE

WHAT IS THE **LARGEST WATERMELON** YOU CAN FIND?

WHAT IS THE **LARGEST ORANGE**?

WHAT IS THE **LARGEST CARROT**?

THE GUINNESS RECORDS:

Largest Watermelon: 197 pounds grown by Ed Weeks of Tarboro, North Carolina. It was 48 inches long.

Largest Orange: 3 pounds 11 ounces grown by Bill Calendine of Tucson, Arizona, in 1977.

Largest Carrot: 11 pounds grown by Bob McEwan of Beeac, Victoria, Australia, in 1967.

MY RECORDS:

WATERMELON ⌣

_____LB._____OZ._____INCHES _____DATE

_____LB._____OZ._____INCHES _____DATE

ORANGE ⌣

_____LB._____OZ._____INCHES _____DATE

_____LB._____OZ._____INCHES _____DATE

CARROT ⌣

_____LB._____OZ._____INCHES _____DATE

_____LB._____OZ._____INCHES _____DATE

MY FRIEND'S RECORDS:

_____

_____

HOW FAR CAN YOU FLY A **PAPER AIRPLANE** ?

HOW LONG CAN YOU KEEP A **PAPER AIRPLANE** IN THE AIR ?

THE GUINNESS RECORD:

Paper Airplanes. Brian Baumann set the indoor distance record of 109 feet 2 inches at Corvallis, Oregon, March 20, 1975. William H. Pryor in Nashville, Tennessee, flew his paper plane for a record 15 seconds. The start must be on level ground and the plane must be hand-held and thrown.

MY RECORDS:

__FEET__INCHES__SECONDS_____DATE

__FEET__INCHES__SECONDS_____DATE

__FEET__INCHES__SECONDS_____DATE

__FEET__INCHES__SECONDS_____DATE

__FEET__INCHES__SECONDS_____DATE

MY FRIEND'S RECORDS:

__FEET__INCHES__SECONDS_____DATE

__FEET__INCHES__SECONDS_____DATE

HOW **LONG** CAN YOU AND YOUR FRIEND PLAY **LEAP FROG**?

THE GUINNESS RECORD:

Leap Frogging. Fourteen students of Hanover High School, Hanover, New Hampshire, covered 555.25 miles in 148 hours, June 4 to 10, 1978.

OUR RECORDS:

_____HOURS_____MINUTES _____DATE

_____HOURS _____MINUTES_____DATE

_____HOURS_____MINUTES_____DATE

_____HOURS_____MINUTES_____DATE

_____HOURS_____MINUTES_____DATE

_____HOURS_____MINUTES_____DATE

THE GUINNESS RECORD:

Grape Catching. Paul Tavila of Dedham, Massachusetts, caught a grape tossed by Mike Weir from 251 feet away on July 19, 1977, on the first throw.

MY RECORDS:

____FEET____INCHES_____DATE

____FEET____INCHES_____DATE

____FEET____INCHES_____DATE

____FEET____INCHES_____DATE

____FEET____INCHES_____DATE

MY FRIEND'S RECORDS:

____FEET____INCHES_____DATE

____FEET____INCHES_____DATE

____FEET____INCHES_____DATE

HOW **FAST** CAN YOU **MAKE** YOUR BED ?

GUINNESS SAYS

Bedmaking. Wendy Wall of Sydney, Australia, holds this record. She made her bed starting with a bare mattress in 29.74 seconds on June 6, 1977.

MY RECORDS:

___MINUTES ___SECONDS_____DATE

___MINUTES ___SECONDS_____DATE

___MINUTES ___SECONDS_____DATE

___MINUTES ___SECONDS_____DATE

___MINUTES ___SECONDS_____DATE

MY FRIEND'S RECORDS:

___MINUTES ___SECONDS_____DATE

___MINUTES ___SECONDS_____DATE

THE GUINNESS RECORD:

Bubble Gum Blowing. Rhodessa Ruffin and Cindy McNeil of California, Andy Barrick of Pennsylvania and Brett Nichols of Georgia all blew bubbles measuring 17 inches across, using 3 pieces of bubble gum each in a contest in 1978.

MY RECORD:

_____INCHES AROUND_____DATE

_____INCHES AROUND_____DATE

_____INCHES AROUND_____DATE

_____INCHES AROUND_____DATE

_____INCHES AROUND_____DATE

MY FRIEND'S RECORD:

_____INCHES AROUND_____DATE

_____INCHES AROUND_____DATE

HOW **LONG** CAN YOU KEEP A HULA HOOP **TWIRLING** AROUND YOUR WAIST ?

HOW **MANY** HULA HOOPS CAN YOU **TWIRL** AT THE **SAME** TIME ?

THE GUINNESS RECORD:

Hula Hooping. The record for continuous twirling is 24½ hours set by Christa Tybus in London, England, June 10 and 11, 1978. The most number of hoops at one time is 62 by Jo Ann Barnes, 15, of Inglewood, California, on October 3, 1976.

MY RECORDS:

____HOURS ____MINUTES_____ DATE

____ HOOPS AT ONE TIME _____DATE

____ HOURS ____MINUTES _____ DATE

____HOOPS AT ONE TIME_____ DATE

____ HOURS ____MINUTES _____ DATE

____HOOPS AT ONE TIME_____DATE

MY FRIEND'S RECORDS:

____HOURS____MINUTES _____ DATE

____HOOPS AT ONE TIME_____DATE

HOW FAR CAN YOU **THROW** A **FRISBEE**®?

THE GUINNESS RECORD:

Frisbee® Throwing. Records for Frisbee® throwing were all set indoors. An Englishman named Steve Harrell threw a Frisbee® 298 feet on July 2, 1978, and a woman in Los Angeles named Monika Lou set the feminine record of 222½ feet on August 24, 1977.

MY RECORDS:

_____FEET_____INCHES_____DATE

_____FEET_____INCHES_____DATE

_____FEET_____INCHES_____DATE

_____FEET_____INCHES_____DATE

_____FEET_____INCHES_____DATE

MY FRIEND'S RECORDS:

_____FEET_____INCHES_____DATE

_____FEET_____INCHES_____DATE

THE GUINNESS RECORD:

Coin Snatching. Gerry Berg, 37, of Vancouver, Canada, in June 1977 caught 97 coins of 25-cent size in his right hand after he had piled them on his right forearm and flipped them out and down. He missed catching a few but he caught 97.

MY RECORDS:

COINS	DATE	COINS	DATE
COINS	DATE	COINS	DATE
COINS	DATE	COINS	DATE
COINS	DATE	COINS	DATE
COINS	DATE	COINS	DATE

MY FRIEND'S RECORDS:

COINS	DATE	COINS	DATE
COINS	DATE	COINS	DATE

WHAT'S THE **LONGEST DISTANCE** YOU CAN **CRAWL** WITHOUT STOPPING?

THE GUINNESS RECORD:

Crawling. The longest continuous crawl with one knee always on the ground is 12½ miles. It was made by Kevin Clavin of Port Jefferson, New York, in 11 hours 55 minutes, May 25 and 26, 1978.

MY RECORD:

_____MILES _____YARDS_____DATE

_____MILES _____YARDS_____DATE

_____MILES _____YARDS_____DATE

_____MILES _____YARDS_____DATE

_____MILES _____YARDS_____DATE

MY FRIEND'S RECORD:

_____MILES _____YARDS_____DATE

_____MILES _____YARDS_____DATE

HOW **LARGE** A **BALL OF STRING** CAN YOU MAKE?

THE GUINNESS RECORD:

Ball of String. Two people share the record for compiling a ball entirely of string—11 feet in diameter, about 5 tons in weight. Francis A. Johnson of Darwin, Minnesota, started his ball in 1950, and Frank Stoeber of Cawker City, Kansas, started his in 1962.

MY RECORDS:

__FEET__INCHES__POUNDS_____DATE

__FEET__INCHES__POUNDS_____DATE

__FEET__INCHES__POUNDS_____DATE

__FEET__INCHES__POUNDS_____DATE

__FEET__INCHES__POUNDS_____DATE

MY FRIEND'S RECORDS:

__FEET__INCHES__POUNDS_____DATE

__FEET__INCHES__POUNDS_____DATE

WHAT'S THE **LARGEST** GAME OF **MUSICAL CHAIRS** YOU HAVE EVER PLAYED?

THE GUINNESS RECORD:

Musical Chairs. The largest game on record started with 1,789 players and ended with a student named Jonathan Winters on the last chair at East High School, Salt Lake City, Utah, in 1977.

MY GROUP'S RECORD:

_____ NUMBER OF PLAYERS _____ DATE

_____ NUMBER OF PLAYERS _____ DATE

_____ NUMBER OF PLAYERS _____ DATE

_____ NUMBER OF PLAYERS _____ DATE

_____ NUMBER OF PLAYERS _____ DATE

THE GUINNESS RECORD:

House of Cards. A 9½-foot-high house of cards was built by Carter Cummins at Westgate Mall, Texas, on June 4, 1977. It had 51 stories and contained 2,206 cards.

MY RECORD:

_____FEET_____INCHES_____DATE

_____FEET_____INCHES_____DATE

_____FEET_____INCHES_____DATE

_____FEET_____INCHES_____DATE

_____FEET_____INCHES_____DATE

MY FRIEND'S RECORD:

_____FEET_____INCHES_____DATE

_____FEET_____INCHES_____DATE

WHAT'S THE **GREATEST** NUMBER OF **JUMPS** YOU'VE EVER MADE ON A **POGO STICK** ?

THE GUINNESS RECORD:

Pogo Stick Jumping. 100,013 jumps in 16 hours 15 minutes without a miss and with only 5-minute rest breaks per hour is the world record. It was set by Steve Ennis, 16, in Chalfont, Pennsylvania, April 1 and 2, 1977.

MY RECORDS:

__JUMPS__ HOURS __ MINUTES____DATE

__JUMPS__ HOURS __ MINUTES ___ DATE

__JUMPS__HOURS __ MINUTES ___ DATE

__JUMPS__HOURS __ MINUTES ___ DATE

__JUMPS__HOURS __ MINUTES____ DATE

MY FRIEND'S RECORDS:

__JUMPS__ HOURS __MINUTES ___ DATE

__JUMPS__ HOURS __ MINUTES___DATE

THE GUINNESS RECORD:

Baton Twirling. Three Tazewell (Virginia) High School majorettes twirled for 50½ hours in December, 1978.

MY RECORDS:

_____ HOURS _____ MINUTES _____ DATE

_____ HOURS _____ MINUTES _____ DATE

_____ HOURS _____ MINUTES _____ DATE

_____ HOURS _____ MINUTES _____ DATE

_____ HOURS _____ MINUTES _____ DATE

MY FRIEND'S RECORD:

_____ HOURS _____ MINUTES _____ DATE

_____ HOURS _____ MINUTES _____ DATE

HOW **FAST** CAN YOU **TIE** THE **SIX** BOY SCOUT KNOTS?

THE GUINNESS RECORD:

Knot Tying. The Boy Scout Handbook requires six knots—the square knot, sheet bend, sheep shank, clove hitch, round turn, and two half hitches and bowline—to be tied on individual ropes. The man who can tie these the fastest is Clinton R. Bailey, Sr., 52, of Pacific City, Oregon. He set the record of 8.1 seconds on April 13, 1977. .

MY RECORDS :

___ MINUTES __SECONDS_____ DATE

___ MINUTES __SECONDS _____ DATE

___ MINUTES__SECONDS_____ DATE

___ MINUTES__SECONDS _____ DATE

___MINUTES __SECONDS_____ DATE

MY FRIEND'S RECORDS:

___ MINUTES__SECONDS_____ DATE

___MINUTES __SECONDS_____ DATE

WHAT'S THE LONGEST TIME YOU'VE BEEN ON **ROLLER SKATES?**

THE GUINNESS RECORD:

Roller Skating Marathon. Randy Reed of Springfield, Oregon, holds the record for roller skating continuously for the longest time...322 hours 20 minutes, June 12 to 16, 1977.

MY RECORDS:

_____ HOURS _____ MINUTES _____ DATE

_____ HOURS _____ MINUTES _____ DATE

_____ HOURS _____ MINUTES _____ DATE

_____ HOURS _____ MINUTES _____ DATE

_____ HOURS _____ MINUTES _____ DATE

MY FRIEND'S RECORDS:

_____ HOURS _____ MINUTES _____ DATE

_____ HOURS _____ MINUTES _____ DATE

HOW **FAST** CAN YOU **RUN** A **THREE-LEGGED** RACE?

THE GUINNESS RECORD:

Three-Legged Race. The record was set in Brooklyn in 1909 at 11 seconds for 100 yards. The racers were Harry L. Hillman and Lawson Robertson, and no one has beaten them since then.

MY RECORDS:

___ SECONDS ___ DATE _____ PARTNERS

___ SECONDS ___ DATE _____ PARTNERS

___ SECONDS ___ DATE _____ PARTNERS

___ SECONDS ___ DATE _____ PARTNERS

___ SECONDS ___ DATE _____ PARTNERS

MY FRIEND'S RECORDS:

___ SECONDS ___ DATE _____ PARTNERS

___ SECONDS ___ DATE _____ PARTNERS

___ SECONDS ___ DATE _____ PARTNERS

WHAT IS YOUR **HIGHEST** SCORE
IN **BOWLING**?
HOW MANY **STRIKES** CAN YOU
MAKE IN A **ROW**?

THE GUINNESS RECORD:

Bowling: 300 is the highest score possible in one game and the only person to roll 26 games of 300 is Elvin Mesger of Sullivan, Missouri. The record for strikes in a row in tournament play is 33 by John Pezzin in Toledo, Ohio, on March 4, 1976.

MY RECORDS :

SCORE	DATE	STRIKES	DATE
SCORE	DATE	STRIKES	DATE
SCORE	DATE	STRIKES	DATE
SCORE	DATE	STRIKES	DATE
SCORE	DATE	STRIKES	DATE

MY FRIEND'S RECORDS :

SCORE	DATE	STRIKES	DATE
SCORE	DATE	STRIKES	DATE

HOW MANY **SIT-UPS** CAN YOU DO ?

HOW MANY **PUSH-UPS** CAN YOU DO ?

THE GUINNESS RECORD:

Sit-Ups and Push-Ups. Richard John Knecht at age 8 did 25,222 sit-ups without stopping for 11 hours 14 minutes in Idaho Falls. His feet were not held nor his knees bent. H. C. Marshall did 9,075 push-ups without stopping for 5 hours in San Antonio, Texas, in September, 1977.

MY RECORDS:

_____ SIT-UPS _____ DATE

_____ PUSH-UPS _____ DATE

_____ SIT-UPS _____ DATE

_____ PUSH-UPS _____ DATE

_____ SIT-UPS _____ DATE

_____ PUSH-UPS _____

MY FRIEND'S RECORDS:

_____ SIT-UPS _____ PUSH-UPS ____ DATE

HOW **LONG** CAN YOU AND YOUR FRIEND **TALK WITHOUT STOPPING ?**

THE GUINNESS RECORD:

Non-Stop Talking. The world record for non-stop talking is 144 hours 4 minutes or more than 6 days. It is held by Tim Harty of Coon Rapids, Minnesota. He began January 27 and ended on February 2, 1975.

MY RECORD:

____ HOURS ____ MINUTES _____ DATE

____ HOURS ____ MINUTES _____ DATE

____ HOURS ____ MINUTES _____ DATE

____ HOURS ____ MINUTES _____ DATE

____ HOURS ____ MINUTES _____ DATE

MY FRIEND'S RECORDS:

_____

_____

HOW **FAR** CAN YOU **JUMP**?

THE GUINNESS RECORD:

Broad Jump. When Bob Beamon of the U.S. leaped 29 feet 2½ inches on June 18 at the 1968 Olympics, held in Mexico City, he broke the previous record by nearly 2 feet.

MY RECORDS:

_____FEET_____INCHES_____DATE

_____FEET_____INCHES_____DATE

_____FEET_____INCHES_____DATE

_____FEET_____INCHES_____DATE

_____FEET_____INCHES_____DATE

MY FRIEND'S RECORDS:

_____FEET_____INCHES_____DATE

_____FEET_____INCHES_____DATE

THE GUINNESS RECORD:

See Saw. The longest anyone see-sawed indoors is 1,101 hours 40 minutes. Two students from Auburn High School in Washington. George Partridge and Tamara Marquez, set this record with only 5 minutes rest after each hour from March 28 to May 18, 1977. The outdoor record is 730½ hours.

MY RECORDS:

_____ HOURS _____ MINUTES _____ DATE

_____ HOURS _____ MINUTES _____ DATE

_____ HOURS _____ MINUTES _____ DATE

_____ HOURS _____ MINUTES _____ DATE

_____ HOURS _____ MINUTES _____ DATE

MY FRIEND'S RECORDS:

_____ HOURS _____ MINUTES _____ DATE

_____ HOURS _____ MINUTES _____ DATE

HOW MANY **BASKETS** CAN YOU MAKE WITHOUT MISSING A SHOT?

THE GUINNESS RECORD:

Basketball Goal-Shooting. This record was set by professional Ted St. Martin, now of Jacksonville, Florida, who made 2,036 free throws in a row without a miss on June 25, 1977.

MY RECORDS:

_____ BASKETS IN A ROW _____ DATE

_____ BASKETS IN A ROW _____ DATE

_____ BASKETS IN A ROW _____ DATE

_____ BASKETS IN A ROW _____ DATE

_____ BASKETS IN A ROW _____ DATE

MY FRIEND'S RECORDS:

_____ BASKETS IN A ROW _____ DATE

_____ BASKETS IN A ROW _____ DATE

_____ BASKETS IN A ROW _____ DATE

THE GUINNESS RECORD:

Golf Ball Balancing. Lang Martin, 16, of Charlotte, North Carolina, succeeded in balancing 6 new golf balls vertically without using any adhesive on July 10, 1978.

MY RECORD:

_____NUMBER OF BALLS _____DATE

_____NUMBER OF BALLS _____DATE

_____NUMBER OF BALLS_____DATE

_____NUMBER OF BALLS_____DATE

_____NUMBER OF BALLS_____DATE

MY FRIEND'S RECORD:

_____NUMBER OF BALLS _____DATE

_____NUMBER OF BALLS _____DATE

HOW FAR CAN YOU **THROW A PLAYING CARD** ?

HOW MANY **PLAYING CARDS** CAN YOU THROW IN A **HAT** ?

THE GUINNESS RECORD:

Card Throwing. Tommy Jackson threw a standard playing card 166 feet at Glenwood School, Phoenix City, Alabama. There is no Guinness record for throwing cards in a hat without missing—maybe you can set one.

MY RECORDS:

_____FEET_____INCHES_____DATE

_____NUMBER IN HAT_____DATE

_____FEET_____INCHES_____DATE

_____NUMBER IN HAT_____DATE

MY FRIEND'S RECORDS:

_____FEET_____INCHES_____DATE

_____NUMBER IN HAT_____DATE

THE GUINNESS RECORD:

Standing Still. The longest that any person has remained absolutely motionless is 5 hours 43 minutes. The record was set by Melody Schick in Dallas, Texas, December 9, 1976.

MY RECORD:

_____HOURS _____MINUTES_____DATE

_____HOURS _____MINUTES_____DATE

_____HOURS _____MINUTES_____DATE

_____HOURS_____MINUTES_____DATE

_____HOURS_____MINUTES_____DATE

MY FRIEND'S RECORD:

_____HOURS ____MINUTES_____DATE

_____HOURS ____MINUTES_____DATE

HOW LONG CAN YOU STAND ON ONE FOOT?

THE GUINNESS RECORD:

Balancing on One Foot. Canadian George Horning stood on one foot for exactly 13 hours without any rests on November 18, 1977. In this feat, no supports can be used and your other foot can't rest against your standing foot.

MY RECORDS:

_____ HOURS _____ MINUTES _____ DATE

_____ HOURS _____ MINUTES _____ DATE

_____ HOURS _____ MINUTES _____ DATE

_____ HOURS _____ MINUTES _____ DATE

_____ HOURS _____ MINUTES _____ DATE

MY FRIEND'S RECORDS:

_____ HOURS _____ MINUTES _____ DATE

_____ HOURS _____ MINUTES _____ DATE

THE GUINNESS RECORD:

Hand Clapping. Four people clapped together for 39 hours 15 minutes in Richmond, Virginia, August 19 and 20, 1977, without stopping. They averaged 140 claps per minute and clapped loud enough to be heard 100 yards away.

MY RECORDS:

_____HOURS_____MINUTES_____DATE

_____PARTNERS

_____HOURS_____MINUTES_____DATE

_____PARTNERS

_____HOURS_____MINUTES_____DATE

_____PARTNERS

_____HOURS_____MINUTES_____DATE

_____PARTNERS

HOW **LONG** CAN YOU KEEP A **KITE** IN THE **AIR**?

THE GUINNESS RECORD:

Kite Flying. The longest recorded continuous flight of a kite was 169 hours in the air, April 30 to May 7, 1977. The Sunrise Inn Team, Fort Lauderdale, Florida, managed by Will Yolen, holds this record.

MY RECORDS:

____HOURS____MINUTES_____DATE

____HOURS____MINUTES_____DATE

____HOURS____MINUTES_____DATE

____HOURS____MINUTES_____DATE

____HOURS____MINUTES_____DATE

MY FRIEND'S RECORDS:

____HOURS____MINUTES_____DATE

____HOURS____MINUTES_____DATE

____HOURS____MINUTES_____DATE

HOW MANY **DOMINOES** CAN YOU PUT IN A ROW AND **TOPPLE** AT **ONE TIME**?

THE GUINNESS RECORD:

Domino Tumble. Michael Cairney of London, England, on June 9, 1979, toppled 169,713 dominoes in Poughkeepsie, N.Y. The dominoes, without the main stream stopping, "walked" up a 7 foot ramp, dialed a telephone and touched off a microswitch that took a Polaroid picture of Cairney. The setup took 14 days and tumbling took 44 minutes 45 seconds.

MY RECORD:

___DOMINOES TOPPLED _____ DATE

___DOMINOES TOPPLED _____ DATE

___DOMINOES TOPPLED _____ DATE

___DOMINOES TOPPLED _____ DATE

___DOMINOES TOPPLED_____ DATE

MY FRIEND'S RECORD:

___DOMINOES TOPPLED_____ DATE

___DOMINOES TOPPLED_____ DATE

THE GUINNESS RECORD:

Horseshoe Pitching. The most ringers in a single game is 175 by Glen Henton of Maquoketa, Iowa, in 1965.

MY RECORDS:

___RINGERS__ DATE __ RINGERS_____ DATE

___RINGERS__ DATE __ RINGERS_____ DATE

___RINGERS__ DATE __ RINGERS_____ DATE

___RINGERS__ DATE __ RINGERS_____ DATE

___RINGERS__ DATE __ RINGERS_____ DATE

MY FRIEND'S RECORDS:

___RINGERS__ DATE __ RINGERS_____ DATE

___RINGERS__ DATE __ RINGERS_____ DATE

HOW LONG CAN YOU **BALANCE** YOUR BICYCLE **WITHOUT MOVING IT?**

THE GUINNESS RECORD:

Bicycle Balancing. David Steel of Tucson, Arizona, stayed still without support while mounted on his bicycle for 9 hours 15 minutes on November 25, 1977.

MY RECORD:

____HOURS ____MINUTES ____DATE

____HOURS ____MINUTES ____DATE

____HOURS ____MINUTES ____DATE

____HOURS ____MINUTES ____DATE

____HOURS ____MINUTES ____DATE

MY FRIEND'S RECORD:

____HOURS ____MINUTES ____DATE

____HOURS ____MINUTES ____DATE

WHAT **PLANT** IN YOUR HOME HAS THE **LONGEST LEAF** ?

THE GUINNESS RECORD:

Largest Plant Leaves. The raffia palm, found on islands in the Indian Ocean, and the Amazonian bamboo palm of South America both have leaf blades measuring as long as 65 feet.

MY RECORD PLANT:

___FEET ___INCHES _____PLANT NAME

___FEET ___INCHES _____PLANT NAME

___FEET ___INCHES _____PLANT NAME

___FEET ___ INCHES _____PLANT NAME

___FEET ___INCHES _____PLANT NAME

___FEET ___INCHES _____PLANT NAME

MY FRIEND'S PLANT:

___FEET ___INCHES _____PLANT NAME

___FEET ___INCHES _____PLANT NAME

HOW **MANY** TIMES CAN YOU SAY
THIS "**TONGUE TWISTER**" QUICKLY:
"THE SIXTH SICK SHEIK'S SIXTH
SHEEP'S SICK."

THE GUINNESS RECORD:

Most Difficult Tongue Twister. "The sixth sick sheik's sixth sheep's sick" is considered to be the most difficult tongue twister in the English language to say quickly without stammering.

MY RECORD:

_____TIMES_____ DATE

_____TIMES_____ DATE

_____TIMES_____ DATE

_____TIMES_____ DATE

_____TIMES_____ DATE

MY FRIEND'S RECORD:

_____TIMES_____ DATE

_____TIMES_____ DATE

WHAT IS THE **BIGGEST FRESH WATER FISH** YOU HAVE EVER **CAUGHT?**

WHAT IS THE **BIGGEST SALT WATER FISH** YOU HAVE EVER **CAUGHT?**

THE GUINNESS RECORD:

Fishing with Rod and Reel. The largest fresh water fish was a 65-pound lake trout caught in Great Bear Lake, Canada, by Larry Dennis on August 8, 1970. For salt water fish the record is 2,664 pounds for a man-eating great white shark that measured 16 feet 10 inches. It was caught by Alf Dean off South Australia in April, 1959.

MY RECORDS:

FRESH WATER~

__POUNDS__ OUNCES_____FISH NAME

__POUNDS__ OUNCES_____FISH NAME

__POUNDS__ OUNCES_____FISH NAME

SALT WATER~

__POUNDS__ OUNCES_____FISH NAME

__POUNDS__ OUNCES_____FISH NAME

MY FRIEND'S RECORDS:

__POUNDS__ OUNCES_____FISH NAME

__POUNDS__ OUNCES_____FISH NAME

WHAT'S THE **LONGEST** GAME OF **CHECKERS** YOU HAVE EVER PLAYED?

THE GUINNESS RECORD:

Longest Game of Checkers. With at least 30 moves per hour by each player, a 1958 match between Dr. Marian Tinsley of the U.S. and Derek Oldbury of Great Britain took 7½ hours.

MY RECORD:

_____HOURS_____MINUTES_____DATE

_____HOURS_____MINUTES_____DATE

_____HOURS_____MINUTES_____DATE

_____HOURS_____MINUTES_____DATE

_____HOURS_____MINUTES_____DATE

MY FRIEND'S RECORD:

_____HOURS_____MINUTES_____DATE

_____HOURS_____MINUTES_____DATE

THE GUINNESS RECORD:

Champion Bird-Watcher. G. Stuart Keith, who is on the staff at the American Museum of Natural History in New York City, has sighted 5,420 species, of the 8,650 known species in the world, over a 30-year period.

MY RECORD:

_____ NUMBER SEEN _____ DATE

_____ NUMBER SEEN _____ DATE

_____ NUMBER SEEN _____ DATE

_____ NUMBER SEEN _____ DATE

_____ NUMBER SEEN _____ DATE

MY FRIEND'S RECORD:

_____ NUMBER SEEN _____ DATE

_____ NUMBER SEEN _____ DATE

HOW **LONG** CAN YOU KEEP A YO-YO IN **MOTION**?

THE GUINNESS RECORD:

Yo-Yo Endurance. 120 hours is the record for keeping a yo-yo in motion and it was set by John Winslow of Gloucester, Virginia, November 23 to 28, 1977.

MY RECORD:

_____HOURS_____MINUTES_____DATE

_____HOURS _____MINUTES_____DATE

_____HOURS_____MINUTES_____DATE

_____HOURS_____MINUTES_____DATE

_____HOURS_____MINUTES_____DATE

MY FRIEND'S RECORD:

_____HOURS   MINUTES_____DATE

_____HOURS   MINUTES_____DATE

THE GUINNESS RECORD:

Table Tennis. The record for playing without a stop is 5 hours 2 minutes 18½ seconds for two players. It was set in New Zealand on November 5, 1977, by John Dufty and Kevin Schick.

MY RECORDS:

__ HOURS __ MINUTES __ SECONDS __ DATE

__ HOURS __ MINUTES __ SECONDS __ DATE

__ HOURS __ MINUTES __ SECONDS __ DATE

__ HOURS __ MINUTES __ SECONDS __ DATE

__ HOURS __ MINUTES __ SECONDS __ DATE

MY FRIEND'S RECORDS:

__ HOURS __ MINUTES __ SECONDS __ DATE

__ HOURS __ MINUTES __ SECONDS __ DATE